The Magic Ring

Written by Russell Punter

Illustrated by Mike and Carl Gordon

How this book works

The story of **The Magic Ring** has been written for you to read with your child. You take turns to read:

You read these words.

Josh and Kip are on the shore. They watch the tide come in. They're stranded on an island.

Josh is sad and he is thin.

Your child reads these words.

You don't have to finish the story in one session. If your child is getting tired, put a marker in the page and come back to it later.

You can find out more about helping your child with this book, and with reading in general, on pages 30-31.

The Magic Ring

Turn the page to start the story.

Josh and Kip are on the shore.
They watch the tide come in.
They're stranded on an island.

Josh is sad
and he is thin.

There's something lying in the sand.
Josh calls out to his pup.

"Is that a big
fat fish, Kip?"

"Be quick then,
dig it up!"

They hope it will be good to eat.
Kip gives his tail a wag.

9

Josh sighs, "It's very pretty..."

But I wish I had a fish.

A flash of light, a cloud of stars —

A big fish
on a dish!

"Hooray, this ring is magic!"
Josh cheers and grins at Kip.

Now Josh and Kip are sailing home,
But soon the wind grows shrill.
"I wish I had a coat," says Josh.

I will get
a chill.

Then comes the most
    enormous crash.
It gives them such a shock.
They slip and slide
    along the deck.

The ship has
hit a rock.

The magic ring goes flying,
And Josh falls in the sea.

"Hop in quick, Kip.
Get it back for me!"

The ring is lost. The ship has sunk.
How gloomy can things get?
Then just in time, they hear a cry:

Now Josh and Kip are safe on board,
And here's a funny thing –

A fish is in the net as well...

And in the fish – the ring!

Puzzle 1

Look at the pictures together and try retelling the story.

1.

2.

3.

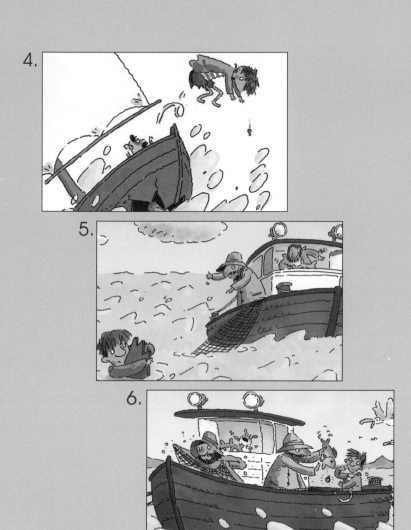

You could talk about what you
might wish for with a magic ring.

Puzzle 2

Match the speech bubbles to the pictures.

1. I will get a chill.

2. Be quick then, dig it up!

3. A big fish on a dish!

4. Hang on to this net!

Puzzle 3

Look at the picture and read the words below. Which five things are in the picture?

- a rock
- a ring
- a can
- a moth
- a ship

- a net
- a dish
- a fish
- a shell
- a dog

Answers to puzzles

Puzzle 1

Use this puzzle to check that your child has understood the story, and have fun discussing what a magic ring might do.

If your child isn't sure what to say, try asking leading questions such as, "Who's this? What are they doing now?" (Of course, there is more than one possible answer.)

Puzzle 3

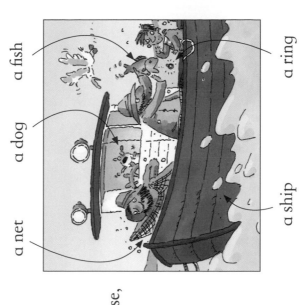

a net   a dog   a fish

a ship   a ring

Puzzle 2

1. I will get a chill. - C
2. Be quick then, dig it up! - D
3. A big fish on a dish! - A
4. Hang on to this net! - B

Guidance notes

Usborne Very First Reading is a series of books, specially developed for children who are learning to read. In the early books in the series, you and your child take turns to read, and your child steadily builds the knowledge and confidence to read alone.

The words for your child to read in **The Magic Ring** introduce these letter-combinations:

It's important for your child to recognize these combinations and their sounds, not just read the letters individually. Be aware that this represents a more challenging stage in their reading, too. Later books in the series gradually introduce more letter-combinations and spelling patterns, while reinforcing the ones your child already knows.

You'll find lots more information about the structure of the series, advice on helping your child with reading, extra practice activities and games on the Very First Reading website,* **www.usborne.com/veryfirstreading**

*US readers go to **www.veryfirstreading.com**

Some questions and answers

- **Why do I need to read with my child?**
  Sharing stories and taking turns makes reading an enjoyable and fun activity for children. It also helps them to develop confidence and reading stamina, and to take part in an exciting story using very few words.

- **When is a good time to read?**
  Choose a time when you are both relaxed, but not too tired, and there are no distractions. Only read for as long as your child wants to – you can always try again another day.

- **What if my child gets stuck?**
  Don't simply read the problem word yourself, but prompt your child and try to find the right answer together. Similarly, if your child makes a mistake, go back and look at the word together. Don't forget to give plenty of praise and encouragement.

- **We've finished, now what do we do?**
  It's a good idea to read the story several times to give your child more practice and confidence. Then you can try reading **Grizzly Bear Rock** at the same level or, when your child is ready, go on to Book 6 in the series.

Edited by Jenny Tyler, Lesley Sims
and Mairi Mackinnon

First published in 2011 by Usborne Publishing Ltd., Usborne House,
83-85 Saffron Hill, London EC1N 8RT, England. www.usborne.com
Copyright © 2011 Usborne Publishing Ltd.